Author Steve Costello is a Burlington native now living in Rutland Town with his wife, Jane. He is an avid bird-watcher and director of public affairs at Central Vermont Public Service.

Illustrator Whitney Lamy lives in Castleton, Vermont, and teaches art at Castleton State College and Poultney Elementary School. When she's not teaching or drawing, she loves to cook for her husband and two daughters.

Special thanks to CV lineworkers Mike Klopchin and Rex Corey, who installed the nesting platforms at Lake Arrowhead. Also, thanks to Steve Parren and Larry Garland and their colleagues at the Vermont Department of Fish and Wildlife for their expertise and hard work.

Finally, thanks to the dozens of people who helped produce this book. Your efforts are appreciated.

Story by Steve Costello
Illustrations by Whitney Lamy
Book design by Laurie Musick Wright

ISBN: 0-9706410-0-1
Library of Congress Card Number: 00-110812

Printed in the United States by Annex Press.
First printing December, 2000.

Central Vermont Public Service

presents

Meeri meets the OSPREYS

A true Vermont story of love and dedication

Maria B

Meeri Meets The Ospreys

Meeri Meets The Ospreys is a true story of love and dedication. Meeri Zetterstrom of Georgia, Vermont, is an animal and bird lover whose efforts to protect ospreys at Lake Arrowhead helped a lone pair of the majestic members of the raptor family successfully raise a family.

Prompted by Meeri, Central Vermont Public Service and the Vermont Department of Fish & Wildlife have assisted ospreys at Lake Arrowhead since 1990, creating buffer zones, educating the public about the endangered birds, and installing nesting platforms for the birds to live on.

Ospreys have spent the spring and summer on a CVPS island at Lake Arrowhead for the past decade, but failed to breed until 1998, when one chick was successfully hatched. In 1999, the parents successfully produced two more offspring who made it from the nest into the wild.

Decades ago, ospreys were nearly wiped out, along with peregrine falcons and several other species, by the use of pesticides, which caused the birds' eggs to fail.

The ospreys, which feed almost exclusively on fish, have slowly returned to Vermont over the past decade. In a majority of cases, the birds have nested on manmade platforms put up to assist them.

At Lake Arrowhead, the birds have been bothered by human interference, some of it intentional, but for the past two years interference has been reduced, and the result has been the first successful osprey breeding at Lake Arrowhead in at least 20 years.

Thanks to the ospreys, I've had the pleasure of getting to know Meeri Zetterstrom, and working with her to protect Lake Arrowhead's ospreys. Vermont owes her a debt of gratitude for her persistence over the years in watching out for the ospreys, and I want to thank her personally for her foresight all those years ago. The Department of Fish & Wildlife is also to be commended for its efforts to protect the birds.

While ospreys might have one day returned to Lake Arrowhead without Meeri's intervention, she deserves enormous credit for her unfailing efforts to help these great birds raise a family so that all of us may enjoy them. This book is based on her efforts, and is a tribute to "Grandma Osprey," as we call her at CVPS.

Bob Young
President and CEO
Central Vermont Public Service

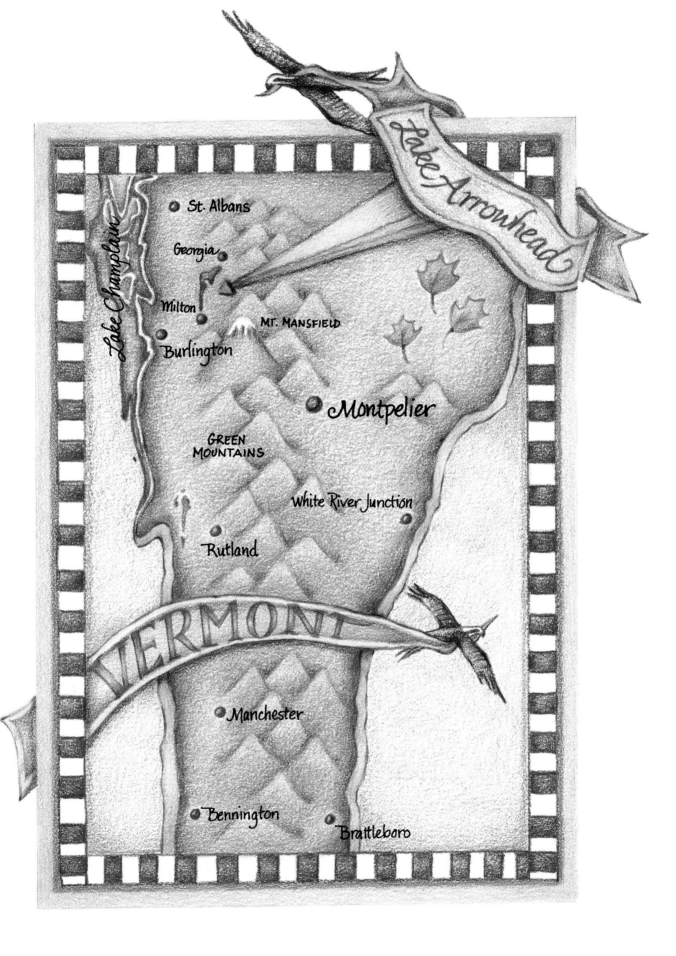

Once upon a time, Mr. and Mrs. Osprey moved to Vermont, and decided to live at Lake Arrowhead. "This would be the perfect place to raise children," Mr. Osprey said as he glided over the water. "The lake is clean, the air is fresh, and there are plenty of fish to feed a family."

Mrs. Osprey agreed. There were almost no other ospreys in Vermont, and Mr. and Mrs. Osprey wanted to be among the first ospreys to call Vermont home. They also wanted to find just the right place to start their family.

"This would be a wonderful place to live," Mrs. Osprey said. "Our children could live safely and happily here."

It was settled. The Ospreys would try to build a nest at Lake Arrowhead.

For that whole spring and summer, the Ospreys lived along the lake, catching fish, and taking in the views from the tops of old pine trees. Each day, they would fly around the lake, looking for just the right spot to build a nest and raise a family.

"How about this spot?" Mr. Osprey said as the couple flew past a dead tree along the lake shore. "It has a nice view of the water, and it's very quiet here."

"That tree is too short," Mrs. Osprey said. "A raccoon could come up and ruin our nest. We must keep looking."

The Ospreys circled the lake again, then stopped to rest. "This looks like a good spot," Mrs. Osprey said as they perched atop a pine tree. "We could build a nest right here."

"It feels kind of creaky," Mr. Osprey said of the tree. "It might be OK, but I think we should keep looking."

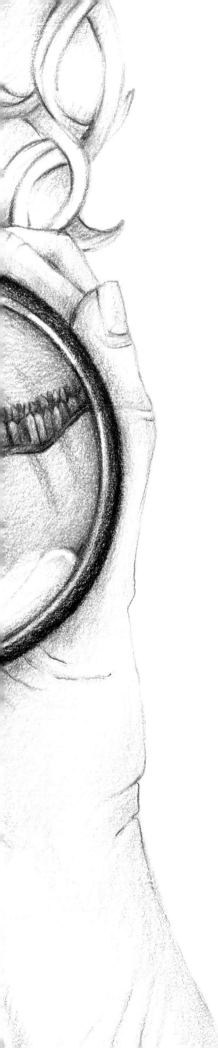

And look they did. They looked along the shore. They looked in the marsh. They looked to the north. They looked to the south.

The Ospreys wanted to find a perfect place to start their family, but they just couldn't agree on where to build their nest.

Up on a hill overlooking the lake, Meeri Zetterstrom sat and watched the Ospreys search. "They are such beautiful birds, with their strong wings and powerful talons," Meeri said to herself. "I hope they decide to stay here and become my neighbors."

One day, as the birds sat on top of a tree near her home, Meeri introduced herself to the Ospreys. "Hello, Mr. and Mrs. Osprey," Meeri said to the birds. "Welcome to the neighborhood. Will you stay?"

"We would love to have a nice neighbor like you," Mr. Osprey told Meeri. "If we can find a suitable spot, we'll stay."

When summer ended, however, the Ospreys were still looking for a good home at the lake. "Oh well," Mr. Osprey said. "Let's fly south for the winter, and come back to Lake Arrowhead next spring. Maybe we'll find a good home then."

"Bye-bye," Meeri said as the couple set off on their journey south. "Come back and see me in the spring."

Meeri was sad. She once lived in Finland, where ospreys were far more common, and she had grown to love the powerful birds.

"I've got to help Mr. and Mrs. Osprey start a family," Meeri said to herself. "There must be a way to provide a perfect nest site for them."

About the country called Finland

- *Finland is a European country, located in the northern reaches of the continent.*

- *Finland didn't gain its independence as a nation until 1917, but there have been human settlements in Finland for at least 100,000 years.*

- *Finland is a land of many lakes — 187,888 of them, with about the same number of islands! Three-quarters of the country is covered by trees.*

- *The climate of Finland is similar to Vermont's climate, with very cold winters and warm summers. The summer is different in northern Finland — the sun does not set there for 73 days!*

- *Finland has 5.2 million people, with two-thirds of them in cities and towns, and the rest living in the countryside.*

- *There are two official languages in Finland, Finnish and Swedish.*

That winter, Meeri thought long and hard. She read everything she could find about ospreys, and decided she needed help.

"Someone has got to give the birds a chance," Meeri said. "They just need a good spot to build their nest."

Meeri called the Department of Fish and Wildlife, and asked the power company to install some big utility poles with nesting platforms on them. "Maybe nature just needs a hand," Meeri said.

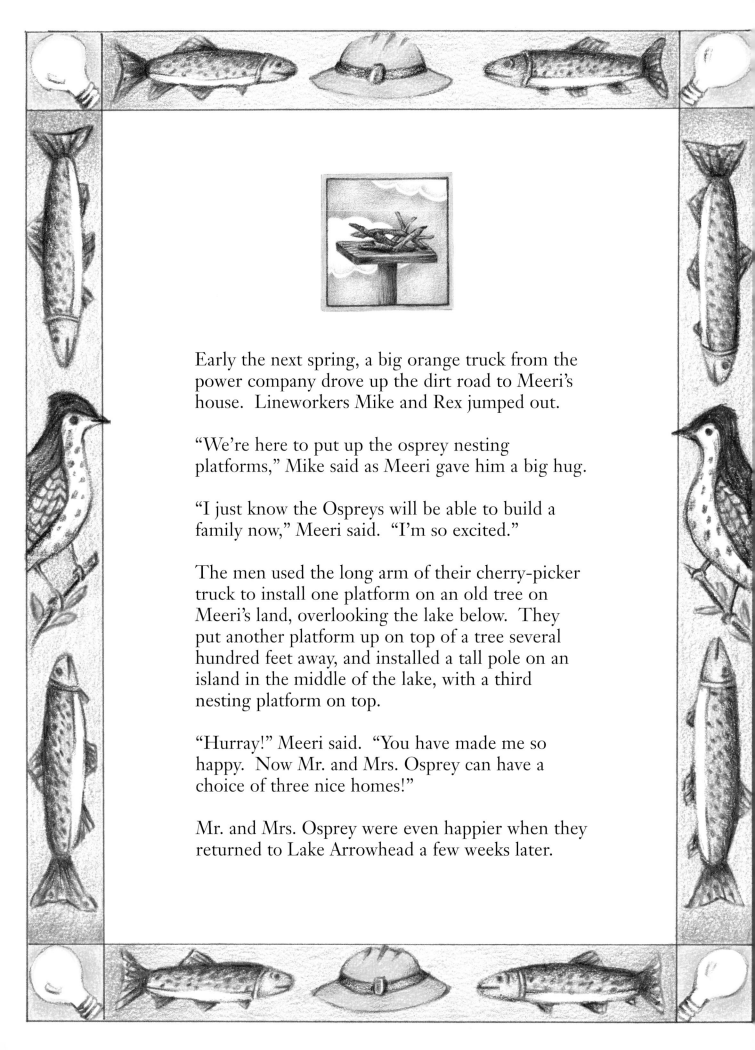

Early the next spring, a big orange truck from the power company drove up the dirt road to Meeri's house. Lineworkers Mike and Rex jumped out.

"We're here to put up the osprey nesting platforms," Mike said as Meeri gave him a big hug.

"I just know the Ospreys will be able to build a family now," Meeri said. "I'm so excited."

The men used the long arm of their cherry-picker truck to install one platform on an old tree on Meeri's land, overlooking the lake below. They put another platform up on top of a tree several hundred feet away, and installed a tall pole on an island in the middle of the lake, with a third nesting platform on top.

"Hurray!" Meeri said. "You have made me so happy. Now Mr. and Mrs. Osprey can have a choice of three nice homes!"

Mr. and Mrs. Osprey were even happier when they returned to Lake Arrowhead a few weeks later.

"Look!" Mrs. Osprey exclaimed as she saw the nesting platform on the island. "Someone has built us a wonderful place to raise our family."

"It's perfect," Mr. Osprey agreed. "Finally we can start to build a nest."

The Ospreys began collecting sticks, carrying them with their feet to the top of the platform.

Meeri smiled and smiled at the Ospreys. "I'm so glad you are building a nest!" she cried. "Now we'll finally have osprey babies."

Not everyone was happy to see the Ospreys. Some people tried to annoy them, buzzing the shore of the island in motorboats. Other people, excited by the opportunity to see the birds for the first time, got too close to the platform and scared Mr. and Mrs. Osprey off.

Spring faded into summer, and the Ospreys decided it wasn't the right time to start a family. "There's too much commotion here," Mrs. Osprey said. "I'm just not comfortable enough to raise chicks with so many people so close to our home."

Mr. and Mrs. Osprey stayed at the lake throughout the summer, then left, still without children, for the winter. "We'll see you next spring," Mrs. Osprey said to Meeri. "We'll miss you!"

The next spring, Mr. and Mrs. Osprey returned to Lake Arrowhead determined to begin their family. They started to build a really big nest on top of the island platform, and collected stick after stick to create tall, thick walls.

Meeri watched them from a safe distance day after day, smiling at the thought that chicks could soon be hatched on the island. Meeri's and the Ospreys' happiness soon faded, when two men in a boat went out to the island and got out of the boat.

"What are they doing?" Meeri said as the men approached the nest. "They're going to upset the Ospreys by getting so close."

That's exactly what they did — and they did it on purpose! One of the men walked to the pole with the nesting platform on top, put his hands around the pole — and shook it!

Up on top, Mrs. Osprey flew away in a panic. "Why would he do this to us?" she cried to Mr. Osprey. "We just want to raise a family."

Up in her house, tears rolled down Meeri's cheeks as she called everyone she could think of to tell them about the mean man on the island. "The poor Ospreys," she said. "Now they may never raise their family here."

Eventually, Mrs. Osprey did lay eggs in the nest. She was as happy as happy could be, but Meeri was even happier. "I'm going to be a grandmother!" she joked. "Finally we'll have baby ospreys!"

Just days later, joy turned to heartache as Mr. and Mrs. Osprey abandoned their eggs. Too many people had gotten too close, and Mrs. Osprey was afraid of the people.

"We'll try again next year," Mrs. Osprey told Meeri, trying to console herself and her neighbor.

That winter, Meeri decided something more had to be done to make sure Mr. and Mrs. Osprey could raise their family at Lake Arrowhead. She called the Department of Fish and Wildlife and the power company again and again. "You've got to do something for Mr. and Mrs. Osprey," Meeri cried. "They need more room."

About Ospreys

- *The scientific name for ospreys is Pandion haliaetus, which means "Pandion's Sea Eagle" in Latin.*

- *An osprey weighs less than a chicken, about four pounds, but has a wingspan of up to six feet!*

- *Ospreys are picky eaters. Their diet is limited almost completely to one thing: fish. .*

- *Ospreys are very strong fliers. Some ospreys have flown all the way across the Mediterranean Sea, fishing along the way for their meals.*

- *Ospreys are the only birds of prey that never capture their prey in the air. Instead, ospreys swoop down over water and catch fish that are swimming just below the surface.*

Early the next spring, workers put up dozens of signs — on the island, on tall posts in the water, at the boat access area and throughout the marsh around the island — asking people to stay away from the birds.

"Let's hope this finally will give the Ospreys the space they need," Meeri said. "If this doesn't work, the Ospreys may never have a family."

Days later, Mr. and Mrs. Osprey returned from their annual winter trip to the South. "Look!" Mr. Osprey shouted when he saw the signs. "Someone is trying to help us!"

"It must be Meeri!" Mrs. Osprey replied. "She's been looking out for us for years!"

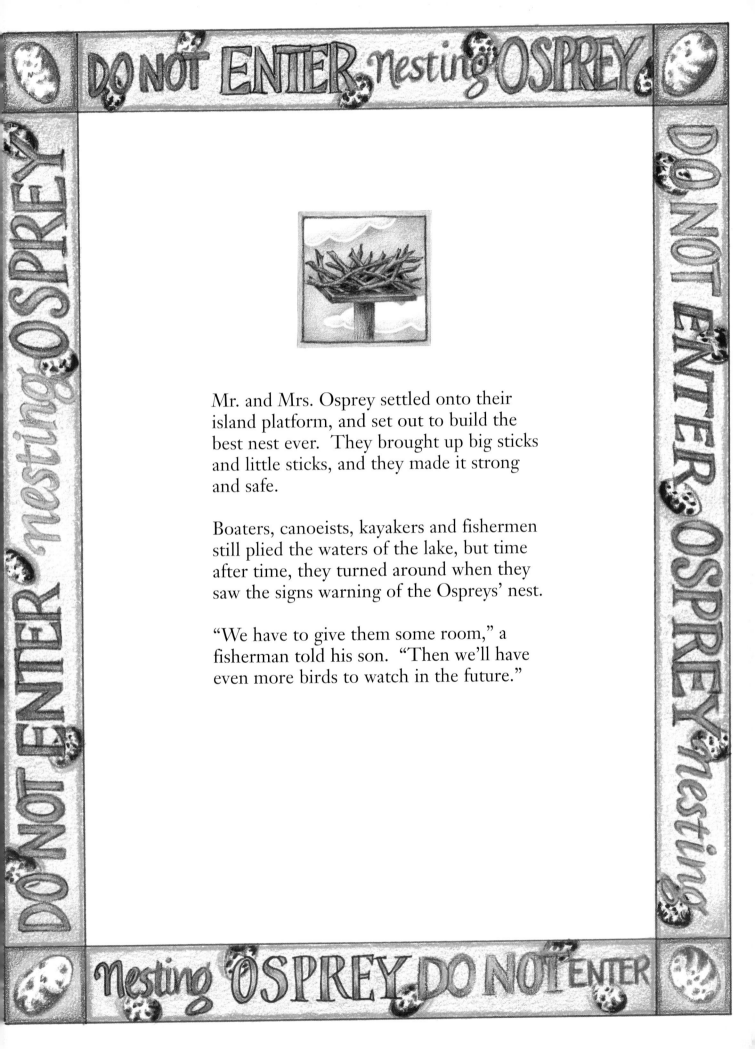

Mr. and Mrs. Osprey settled onto their island platform, and set out to build the best nest ever. They brought up big sticks and little sticks, and they made it strong and safe.

Boaters, canoeists, kayakers and fishermen still plied the waters of the lake, but time after time, they turned around when they saw the signs warning of the Ospreys' nest.

"We have to give them some room," a fisherman told his son. "Then we'll have even more birds to watch in the future."

Mrs. Osprey laid an egg, and sat on it for days, then weeks. Each day, Mr. Osprey would fly out over the water until he spied a fish, then catch it and bring it back for Mrs. Osprey to enjoy.

"This time we'll succeed," Mrs. Osprey told him one morning. "I can just feel it."

Mr. Osprey was growing weary of the hard work of building nests each year, only to fail in hatching any young. "I hope you're right, Sweetheart," he said to Mrs. Osprey. "It's time for us to have a family."

One day later, Mrs. Osprey felt the egg begin to move beneath her. It wiggled just a little at first, then a little more. Then a tiny beak poked a hole through the shell as Mr. and Mrs. Osprey watched.

Soon, the tiny bird's head was sticking out of the eggshell. "Mommy! Daddy!" the young chick cried.

Please
KEEP OUT!
OSPREYS
NESTING

Mr. and Mrs. Osprey helped the chick out of her shell and gave her some food. Within minutes, she was standing up and walking around in the nest.

"She's so beautiful and strong," Mr. Osprey said. "She has to have a name that fits her. What should we call her?"

"Meeri!" Mrs. Osprey replied. "We'll call her Meeri!"

The End